Marvin the Mole
& the
Queen's Jubilee

To Xavier,

With best wishes,

Gerald Watts

March 2022

For Mary Watts

Marvin the Mole and the Queen's Jubilee

Text copyright © Gerald Watts 2012
Illustrations copyright © Lisa Fox 2012

First Published 2012

Published by The Pightle Publishing
Burthorpe Green, Bury St Edmunds, IP29 5DA
http://thepightlepublishing.co.uk

Printed by Premier Printers Limited
Boldero Road, Moreton Hall, Bury St Edmunds, Suffolk IP32 7BS
Telephone: 01284 767552

ISBN   978-0-9570558-0-3

Marvin the Mole
& the
Queen's Jubilee

Gerald Watts • Lisa Fox

Marvin, though small and almost blind,

Was not the shy, retiring kind.

He was determined to have fun,

To see the sky, to feel the sun

On his back and the wind in his face.

He would not believe the only place

That moles were safe was underground

Away from where the slightest sound

Brought long-nosed dogs with digging paws,

Birds with beaks and cats with claws.

His Mum and Dad time and again

Took the trouble to explain.

'Down here it may be cramped and rough

But on the surface life is tough

Especially for moles. Believe us, son,

We're not against you having fun

But you are too curious and bold,

So you must do as you are told.'

For quite a while Marvin was good,

Playing only where a young mole should,

But one day, tunnelling along

With no thought of doing wrong,

He heard the most delightful noise,

The shouts and cheers of girls and boys.

He asked himself 'What can it be?

I'll just go take a look and see.'

So up he went, broke through the turf,

Emerging in a shower of earth.

It was school sports day afternoon,

The fifty metre egg and spoon,

The children racing for the line

When up popped Marvin in lane nine.

Oh, what a sight! What a surprise!

The rushing feet, the staring eyes!

Marvin panicked, dived for cover.

Two children crashed into each other.

Another tried to dodge and slipped

As one by one the runners tripped,

Got tangled up in arms and legs,

Discarded spoons and scrambled eggs.

The teacher glared into the hole.

'One day I'm going to get that mole!'

All next week Marvin stayed home,

Minding no business but his own,

Until on Saturday afternoon

He heard a most uplifting tune.

An organ played, hymns were sung

And all the steeple bells were rung.

Corks were popping, people laughing.

'That sounds fantastic,' said young Marvin,

'I've never heard such joyful laughter,

Such cries of 'Happy Ever After'.

I won't cause trouble like last week.

I'll just go up and take a peek.'

The handsome groom and blushing bride

Stood arm in arm. On either side

Stretched row on row of their relations

Gathered for the celebrations,

Dressed up in fancy frocks and hats,

Silk scarves, lace gloves and smart cravats.

The photographer had just said 'Please

Everyone, keep still. Big smiles. Say cheese.'

When all of a sudden Marvin appeared,

As scruffy as a pirate's beard,

Sending grass and bits of dirt

Spattering their well-ironed shirts.

The ladies shrieked to see the messes

Made upon their lovely dresses.

The photographer stamped upon the hole.

'One day I'm going to get that mole!'

A fortnight passed. Marvin felt sad.

Perhaps being adventurous was bad.

But, young and full of life, he soon grew bored.

'It's time,' he said, 'that I explored

Over the hill.' So off he went,

Digging to his heart's content

Until, at last, all tired and hot,

He found the perfect picnic spot.

'Here is nice. The ground is soft

And no strange noises from above.

Surely nothing can go wrong?

I'll just look round. I won't be long.'

A silent crowd surveyed the scene:

A golfer on the eighteenth green.

This putt to win the Player's Cup.

This putt to lift the trophy up.

The golfer eyed the line, stood tall,

Breathed deep and gently tapped the ball.

It set off straight towards the hole

When suddenly a pink-nosed mole

Emerged from deep beneath the ground

And sent the ball the wrong way round.

The golfer knelt and thumped the hole.

'One day I'm going to get that mole.'

This time Marvin had learnt his lesson.

He asked his Mum and Dad's permission

And only went to quiet places:

No stamping feet, no angry faces.

But all that changed a few weeks later

When our restless little excavator

Dug beneath a flower bed

To breathe the scent and rest his head.

He made a den and settled in.

He gave his fingernails a trim.

He ate his lunch and took a nap,

Snoozing in peace, not knowing that

He slept beside a big marquee

Where the Queen was due for tea.

The tinkle of spoons, the chink of cups,

The chatter of guests woke Marvin up.

The Prime Minister took the microphone,

Announcing in a solemn tone:

'We salute Her Royal Majesty

On this her special Jubilee.'

Marvin heard. His heart beat faster.

This might mean triumph or disaster.

Surely he could see the Queen

And sneak away without being seen?

Slowly, feeling very nervous,

Marvin came up to the surface.

A waiter with a tray of cakes

Who normally made no mistakes

Stumbled as the ground gave way.

Unfortunately this sent the tray

Spinning wildly through the air.

The cakes and buns flew everywhere.

The guests looked round, alarmed, surprised

To see a pair of blinking eyes.

The golfer was the first to speak,

Wiping icing from his cheek,

'The mole! It's time for my revenge.'

'Oh, let me help you, my good friend,'

Said the photographer with glee.

The teacher shouted, 'Yes, and me!'

One jumped, one leapt, the other pounced.

'You dare to come here unannounced.

Making trouble. Messing up the tent.

It's time you got your punishment.'

With that they grabbed the little mole

And shoved him in a serving bowl.

Marvin was scared. He was afraid.

O, how he wished that he had stayed

At home near to his Mum and Dad.

He felt alone. He felt so sad.

Big tears rolled down his little cheeks

Leaving damp and muddy streaks.

The Queen stepped forward gracefully.

'What's all the fuss? Now, let me see.'

She lifted up the serving bowl.

She saw the wretched, guilty mole.

'In all my reign of many years

I've never seen such heartfelt tears.

Though living cautiously is fine,

Being curious is no crime.

Despite the damage to my garden,

I grant this mole a royal pardon.'

A Royal Footman dressed in black

Wiped him down and took him back,

Back to his worried Mum and Dad

Who hugged and kissed their little lad.

Marvin hugged them tight and said

Perhaps he'd like to go to bed,

And promised he'd take extra care

When playing in the open air.